YOGI
on a
JOURNEY

Written by

Shlomi Almoslinos

Illustrated by

Moran Reudor

Yogi on a Journey by Shlomi Almoslinos
Copyright 2022 by Shlomi Almoslinos ©

yogi.on.a.journey1@gmail.com

Illustrator: Moran Reudor
Editors: Lucinda Dodds & Emma Dobinson - Flying Pants Editing
Cover design: Melinda Martin
Layout design: Minhajul Islam

Published by Yoga4kids- Sydney Pty Ltd

ISBN:
Hardcover: 978-0-6453816-1-0
Paperback: 978-0-6453816-2-7
Kindle eBook: 978-0-6453816-0-3

DISCLAIMER:
The author, illustrator, and publisher accept no responsibility for any injuries
or losses that may result from practicing yoga outlined in the story book.
Please ensure your own safety and safety of the children.

Yogi on a Journey is an adventure for children of all ages. It is a fun and playful way to discover the benefits of the Sun Salutation, also called **Surya Namaskar**, the most important and beautiful sequence in any flow of Yoga practice.

Performed regularly, this set of 12 poses (or **asanas**) increases flexibility, strength, coordination and body awareness. Practising the Sun Salutation for ten minutes every morning will uplift your child's mood and boost their day with joy.

Namaste

With gratitude and
deep love to my daughter Gaia,
the sun of our world.

INSTRUCTIONS
FOR PARENTS AND EDUCATORS

It is best to read this story while the children sit in a circle.

Follow the instructions and illustrations to perform each Yoga pose you find along the way.

There is no need to stay in the pose until the next one, so practise the pose, get back to a sitting position and keep on reading.

After a while, when the children are familiar with the poses, they can flow from one pose to the next without stopping in between.

Breathing correctly is important in any Yoga practice.
However, when teaching children, I believe that we need to simplify things.
So, as a rule of thumb, guide them to inhale while the chest is expanding or the body is stretching and to exhale while bending or the body is relaxing.

If that seems too complicated, just do what feels right in your body!

Lastly, feel free to improvise, add more poses or even invent new ones.

Transform it into a game but always keep it playful and fun.

Now, let the journey begin...

Once upon a time, in a faraway land called India, lived the Yogis. The Yogis were wise souls who left the cities to live a simple life, surrounded by nature.

They observed the movements of the Sun and the Moon, the animals, trees and birds.

By watching them, the rhythm and harmony of life was revealed and the Yogi's wisdom and kindness evolved.

On the Equinox, when day and night are of equal length, the Yogis decided to send one of their clan on a journey.

Aryan was a young Yogi, who like many children his age, had many hobbies. Aryan loved playing his flute and spent many hours creating colourful sand mandalas. Aryan was happy in nature, for it filled him with a sense of serenity. Most of all, Aryan enjoyed playing with his friends, inventing new yoga poses with them, to strengthen both their bodies and minds.

Aryan volunteered for the journey because he sensed that it was his time to shine.

He was ready to find the courage to face the unknown.

As a Yogi, Aryan knew that meaningful lessons could be learned from facing his fears, so he nervously and excitedly prepared himself for whatever the future held.

It was to be an extraordinary, but
challenging journey to thank the Sun for
all the light, warmth and life she provided.
And so, Aryan set off on his mission,
brave as brave can be.

The Sun was high in the sky and Aryan
realised that the closest he could get to
give her thanks, would be to climb the
highest mountain in the Himalayas
(and the whole world),
Mount Everest.

FIRST POSE: Mountain Pose

SANSKRIT: Tadasana (Tah-dah-sa-nah)

INSTRUCTIONS: Stand up tall, bring your feet together and stretch your arms down by your sides, pointing your fingers to the floor. Breath in, expand your chest.

TIP: Feel the ground beneath your feet. Stay stable, strong and quiet like a mountain.

Aryan found the journey confronting.
It was hard work climbing the steep mountain alone,
so he decided to call on his elephant friend, Ananda, for help.
'I could not be more thrilled to take part in fulfilling your glorious
destiny,' Ananda rejoiced.
Aryan gently climbed onto his friend's back and pointed
towards the top of the mountain to show her the direction
of their trek.
Ananda smiled and raised her trunk
towards the Sun.

SECOND POSE: Elephant Looking Up Pose
SANSKRIT: Urdhva Hastasana (OORD-vah hahs-TAHS-uh-nuh)
INSTRUCTIONS: Stand up tall like you did in Mountain Pose.
Bring your hands together in front of your hips and look up.
Lift your arms above your head up to the Sun.

TIP: Imagine that your arms are the elephant's trunk.
Feel how long the trunk is as you stretch your
arms as high as you can.

Aryan and Ananda rode for days.
They carefully navigated their way across rice fields,
deep forests and rocky trails.
One afternoon they noticed a sparkling pond along the way.
As the light beamed through the water Aryan and his friend
came to the edge of the clear, cold water and Ananda took
a long drink with her trunk.

TIP: You can bend your knees a little to make it easier.

THIRD POSE: Elephant Drinking Water Pose
SANSKRIT: Uttanasana (Oot-tan-AHS-anah)
INSTRUCTIONS: Now the elephant drops her trunk downwards, so fold your upper body forward and try to reach your toes.

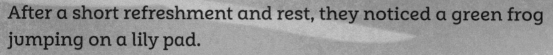

After a short refreshment and rest, they noticed a green frog
jumping on a lily pad.

'Where are you going?' the frog croaked.

'We are on our way to the top of the mountain to show our
gratitude to the Sun,' Aryan answered.

'What are you grateful for?' wondered the frog.

'We are grateful for all the light, warmth and life the Sun
brings to our world,' Ananda explained.

TIP: It is fun and easy to jump like a frog! Try to jump forwards, backwards and then as high as you can. 'RIBBIT!'

FOURTH POSE: Frog Pose
SANSKRIT: Malasana (Mala-asana)
INSTRUCTIONS: Bend your knees and come down into a squat position, like a frog. Place your palms on the floor between your legs.

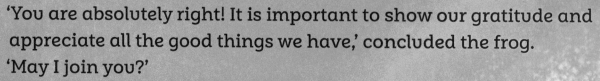

'You are absolutely right! It is important to show our gratitude and appreciate all the good things we have,' concluded the frog.
'May I join you?'
'We would love to have you join our adventure,' responded Aryan.
Suddenly, there was loud barking that came from the reeds and a spectacular dog appeared. 'May I join you, too?'
'Of course! You are both more than welcome,' the Yogi laughed.

TIP: Imagine that you are stretching your arms and legs like a dog that has just woken up.

FIFTH POSE: Downward-Facing Dog Pose
SANSKRIT: Adho Mukha Svanasana
(AH-doh MOO-kah shvah-NAHS-anna)
INSTRUCTIONS: Bend down and place your hands and knees on the floor. Lift your hips and step your feet back to create an upside-down **V** shape with your bottom high in the air. Straighten your legs, and keep your head relaxed between your arms.

Aryan and his new bunch of friends travelled together on their special quest towards the top of the mountain, to greet the Sun and thank her for guiding them.

One morning, as the Sun was rising, they sat together on the edge of a cliff for meditation.
A cat quietly joined them and shared her story.
With breathtaking views all around them the cat told the colourful gang that she was a mindfulness master.
'Mindfulness is simply being aware of what is happening in every single moment,' the cat explained.

SIXTH POSE: Cat Pose

SANSKRIT: Marjariasana (Mar-jaree-asana)

INSTRUCTIONS: First, sit on your knees, then bend forward and place your hands on the floor, fingers spread evenly, look forward.
Now, take in a deep breath (inhale) and slowly lift your head to gaze up.
Then, while breathing out (exhale), gently drop your chin to your chest and look at your belly as you arch your back towards the sky.

TIP: Make quiet meowing sounds and wiggle your tail.

The cat had heard about their journey and wished to join them. Without hesitation, everyone agreed and she then taught them her mantra:

'With my back straight and an open chest,
my body always feels the best.'

They all repeated this empowering phrase that lifted their mood and thanked the cat for sharing her wisdom.

Then, unexpectedly, they spied a cobra snake, slithering towards them.

TIP: Take a deep breath and hiss like a snake, moving your head from side to side.

SEVENTH POSE: Snake Pose
SANSKRIT: Bhujangasana (boo-jang-GAHS-anna)
INSTRUCTIONS: Lay down on your tummy, stretch your legs back. Feel the ground underneath your body.
Place your palms face down on the ground next to your shoulders, push your hands to the floor and slowly lift up your chest.

For a moment, they all froze in fear.
Should they stay still, or run away?

Then the snake spoke up, 'Please don't be afraid!
The entire village speaks about your marvellous journey.
I would like to join you, to represent the reptile family and show
our deep appreciation to the Sun, for all that she does for us.'

'I am so happy to hear that, and you are most welcome on our
pilgrimage,' said Aryan.
'We are close to the top of the mountain now.
By midday tomorrow we will be able to share our
message of love with the Sun.'
Everyone cheered with excitement.

INSTRUCTIONS

To complete this series of poses called Surya Namaskar, we need to do the same poses we have just learned but BACKWARDS.

So, do each pose while reading aloud the name of each animal.

Finish as we started, with the Mountain Pose

The following day, Aryan and his majestic parade of friends finally arrived. Reflecting back on the arrival of each friend on the journey, and the friendships they formed, Aryan could fully appreciate how fortunate he was with all his friends by his side:

A SNAKE, A CAT, A DOG, A FROG, AND AN ELEPHANT.

All stood on the top of the mountain.

They formed a circle, and showed a prayer of gratitude toward the Sun.

And the Sun smiled down, sending rays of light towards their hearts.

The Sun then spoke warmly to the merry band of friends.

'Each of you is unique and magnificent. You hold the power to bring light, warmth and love to yourself and your surroundings.'

The Sun continued, shining rays of love outwards.

'Whenever you feel that you need more strength or courage, take a moment to remember this voyage and the friends you met along the way. Then, simply do all the poses you have learned on this spectacular journey.

You can call them the **Sun Salutation**. This is my humble gift to you.'

They all joined hands together at the heart, closed their eyes, chanted 'Namaste' simultaneously and bowed.

Sun Salutation

CONTRIBUTORS AND ACKNOWLEDGMENTS

I would like to pay my deepest gratitude and respect to all my Yoga teachers, past and present. Especially to:

Osnat Israeli for planting the inspirational seed for this book and for being a wealth of knowledge that shines her valuable guidance like the Sun.

Anat Zahor for opening the door to the world of Yoga and revealing its wonder.

Michael Gluzman for bringing so much wisdom and kindness to his teachings and surroundings.

Gopala Amir Yaffa for being a free soul and teaching me how to fly.

Amanda Fuzes for setting my path as a Yoga teacher in Australia, for believing in me and being a true role model Yogi.

Big thank you to the one and only, my awesome wife, **Bat-el Stoler**.
The magic, loving force of our family.
Supporting from the back, leading from the front and hugging from the sides.
You are the one who really sent a Yogi on a journey.

Special thanks to my sister **Dana Almozlinos**, who kept this dream alive. This book is no longer in the back of the drawer (or Dropbox) thanks to you.

I can't sing **Moran Reudor's** praises enough!
I am so lucky to have you on board along this journey, with your outstanding skills and support in bringing my words to life full of colours.

Gigantic thanks to Lucinda and Emma from **Flying Pants Editing** for revealing truly magnificent skills while upgrading this journey and story to the place where it belongs. Working with you was exactly what I subconsciously wanted and realistically needed and for that I am forever grateful.

Kudos to **Melinda Martin & Minhajul Islam**, the most wonderful and dedicated designers who took care of finalising both the full Book Cover and the Book Layout for printing.

All the **CHILDREN**, either from my preschools or the Yoga lessons.
Throughout the world and throughout the years.
You are the reason for this journey.
Thank you for being part of it.

And of course, to my **PARENTS**, for your love, unconditional support and for giving me the opportunities and experiences that have made me who I am.
Love you!!

MORE THANKS

Miri Friedman, Kathryn Ferguson, Beulah & Nicole Ezra, Matthew George, Maya Shafer, Kelly & Théo Nance, Lena Shur, Lior Aviram, Kika, Kimberly Hitchens of Booknook.biz and all the kickstarter backers - the book would not be the same without you.

Finally, I want to thank **EVERYONE** who went for a journey to bring light, warmth and love for themselves and their surroundings.

CPSIA information can be obtained
at www.ICGtesting.com
Printed in the USA
LVHW071131020322
712109LV00006B/40